mobiles
finger puppets
on-line
101
spinners
101 ideas machine
games
postcards
easy-peasy
things to do
with your
computer
music-maker
jokes
dressing up
cyberpet corner
KINGFISHER

KINGfISHER
Kingfisher Publications Plc
New Penderel House, 283–288 High Holborn,
London WC1V 7HZ

First published by Kingfisher Publications Plc 1998
10 9 8 7 6 5 4 3 2 1

A CIP catalogue record for this book is available from the British Library

ISBN 0 7534 0282 3

Printed in Hong Kong / China

THE EASY-PEASY TEAM

Tony Wheeler (The Living 101 Ideas Machine),
Ben Short (The Program-Wizard),
Clare Oliver (Little Miss Top Organisation),
Sarah Goodwin (Sparkling Fairy of Design)
Tom Baird (Big Mr Organisation)
With thanks to Karen Baird, Adam Hibbert, Caroline Jackson, Peter Jewell, James Wheeler and Marc Wilson.

Tony used to be a teacher until he started thinking up clever things to do with computers and decided to do that instead. He also wrote **101 Amazing Things** with Ben.

Ben is Tony's writing partner. He is a master of tricky program-writing and his proudest moment was when the **cyberpet** looked up at him and said...'Pizza!'

Clare aka The Voice of **easy-peasy**. She holds everything together, sorts out all the words and keeps the others on their toes! She helped Tony and Ben to make **101 Amazing Things**.

Sarah cast a magic spell over the book to make it sparkly and beautiful to look at. She used special fairyland colours and made sure that Jo and Woody knew what to draw.

And finally, not forgetting...
the most hilarious clip art and cartoons from the two most brilliant illustrators: **Jo Moore** and **Woody**

contents

information for parents

Here at last are a book and CD which are specially designed to be used together.

101 easy-peasy things...

- ★ introduces children to the fantastic world of creative discovery awaiting them inside their computer
- ★ gives young children hours of fun and entertainment
- ★ helps children to master invaluable IT skills

101 easy-peasy things offers:

- ★ play on-screen activities
- ★ print-and-play activities
- ★ lots and lots of free clip art
- ★ fast Internet links

System Requirements

Windows

If you have a Windows PC, you will need:

- ★ 486SX/50 MHz processor or better
- ★ Windows 3.1 or better
- ★ 640 x 480 monitor with 256-colour SVGA
- ★ CD-ROM drive
- ★ sound card
- ★ speakers/headphones
- ★ 8MB RAM (16MB recommended)
- ★ printer
- ★ a modem and Internet account (if you want to use the Internet fast links)

Macintosh

If you have a Mac, you will need:

- ★ 040 processor or better
- ★ System 7.1 or above
- ★ 640 x 480 monitor set to 256 colours
- ★ CD-ROM drive
- ★ speakers (usually built-in) or headphones
- ★ 5MB available RAM (7MB recommended)
- ★ printer
- ★ a modem and Internet account (if you want to use the Internet fast links)

It's recommended that early computer learning is an experience that children share with their parents. As their confidence increases, children can begin to play alone. Parents' Corner (see page 6) gives you the facility to set computer options to suit your child's ability.

Installing the disk

When installing the CD, you can choose between minimum install or full install.

minimum install
takes up less hard disk space (6MB), but runs more slowly.

full install
takes up more hard disk space (60MB), but runs much quicker and is particularly recommended for slower machines or machines with slow CD-drives.

Windows 95

★ set your computer to 256 colours (see your computer user manual)
★ click on 'Start' on the task bar
★ click on 'Run' and type 'd:\setup' (where 'd' is the letter of your CD-drive)
★ click 'OK' or press 'enter'
★ select either full install or minimum install

Windows 3.1

★ set your computer to 256 colours (see your computer user manual)
★ open the File Manager
★ click on 'Run' and type 'd:\setup' (where 'd' is the letter of your CD-drive)
★ click 'OK' or press 'enter'
★ select either full install or minimum install

Installation is easy-peasy if you follow these simple instructions...

Macintosh

★ double-click on the install icon
★ select either full install or minimum install

Getting started

Windows 95

★ click on 'Start' in the task bar
★ in Programs, go to '101 Easy Peasy Things'
★ click on '101 Easy Peasy Things' or 'Clipart Picker'

Windows 3.1

★ go to the Program Manager group '101 Easy Peasy Things'
★ double-click on '101 Easy Peasy Things' or 'Clipart Picker'

Macintosh

★ open your hard drive
★ open the folder called '101 Easy Peasy'
★ double-click on '101 Easy Peasy' or 'Clip Art Picker'

handy hints for parents

Customize the CD settings in Parents' Corner to make sure that **101** suits your computer – and your child's ability.

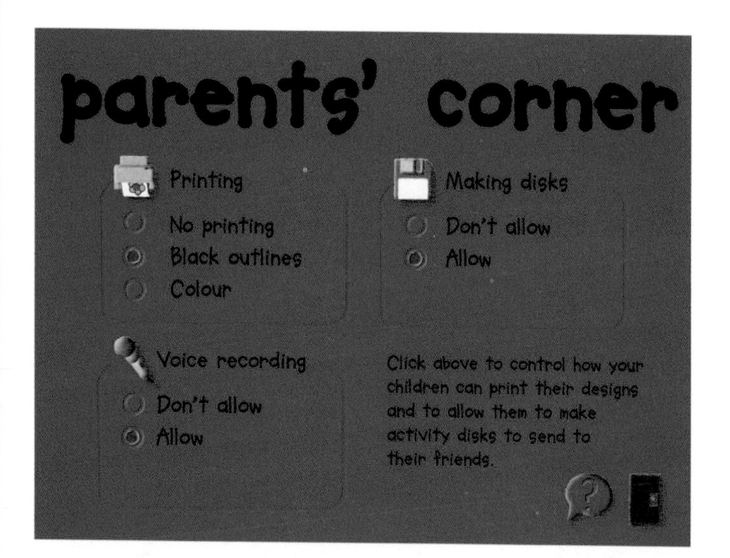

Looking after your child

Make sure your child's first computer experiences are happy – and healthy.

Eyes & ears

★ Do not let your child sit too close to the screen.

★ Make sure the room's lighting is not reflecting off the screen.

★ Make sure your child takes regular breaks from looking at the screen.

★ Check the sound levels if your child is using headphones.

Hands & wrists

★ Make sure your child is sitting *in front* of the computer.

★ Make sure your child's elbows are level with the keyboard.

★ Use wrist supports with the computer.

★ Make sure your child sits up straight at the computer so they are not putting any weight on their hands or wrists.

Looking after your computer

Even though most computers are quite robust, there are some things you need to bear in mind to make sure that everything keeps running smoothly.

Slips and spills

Spilt drinks or crumbs can seriously damage your keyboard, mouse or disks. Make sure your child doesn't put down drinks and snacks near the computer.

Heat and dust

Computers need to keep cool, so keep them away from very high temperatures. Dust can be a problem and should be avoided.

Back & posture

★ Seat your child at a chair with height adjustment and make sure everything is within their reach.

★ Make sure your child rests their feet on the floor.

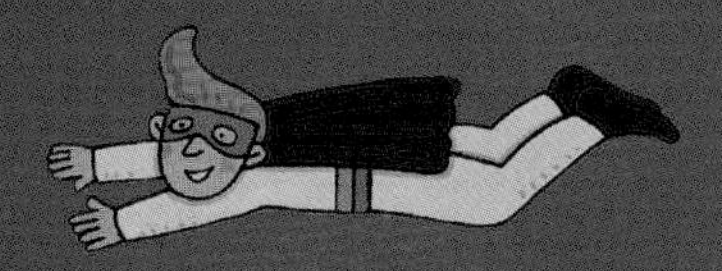

★ Make sure your child takes regular breaks. Some computers allow you to set an alarm to remind you to stop at regular intervals. Get your child to move away from the computer and have a shake down.

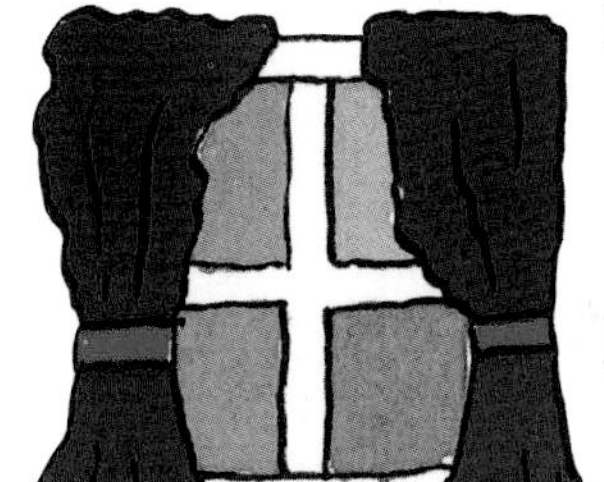

Screen burn-out

If you leave the same picture on your screen for a long time, it could cause serious damage. Screen savers such as After Dark will turn your screen off automatically when it is not being used.

Computer viruses

As your child swaps activity disks with friends, it's possible that your computer could be exposed to viruses. These can upset or even destroy your files, so it is recommended that you install some anti-virus software, such as The Norton Antivirus (for PCs) or Symantec AntiVirus (for Macs).

Better safe than sorry

Always supervise young children closely when they are using computers. If you have valuable work on your computer, it's a good idea to keep copies as back-up. You can also install security software, such as Folder Guard (for PCs) or At Ease (for Macs) which stop your child from being able to access them.

introduction

Computers are **easy-peasy** to use once you get the hang of them. With this book and CD you'll soon be using your PC to write music, make games and lots more!

First of all, start up the CD (ask an adult to show you how the first time).

1. Choose how to play:

★ play on-screen
★ print-and-play
★ play on-line (ask a grown-up to help)

Click here to get to the six on-screen activities. These are things to do or games to play on your computer. See page 12 for more details.

Click here for colouring-in fun. These six activities are special templates to design and print out. See page 24 for more details.

To play on-line, you'll need to ask an adult for help. See page 38 for details. This button's just to remind you that you can!

101 easy-peasy things

play on-screen

print-and-play

play on-line

parents' corner

Click on the door to go back one screen or to quit.

This is for adults so they can match the settings on the CD to match your machine.

Click here to make a player disk to send to a friend or to play a disk. See page 10 for more details.

Click on the speech bubble if you want to hear the spoken instructions again.

2. Choose an activity to play.
Click on the button that shows the one you want.

3. Choose a button.

★ Click on an empty button to start a new activity. You'll be asked to choose a picture. Remember which picture you choose – this is the 'file name' of your activity.

Use these arrows to change the picture until you find one you like.

Press here if you change your mind and don't want to start a new activity.

When you find the one you want, click 'OK'.

Handy hints

★ If you share your computer, it's a good idea to always choose the same picture. That way, you'll remember which activities YOU made.

★ Pick a button with a picture on it to open a finished, saved activity.

★ When all six buttons are full, you'll have to throw one away before you can make anything new. Drag the picture on the button into the bin.

If you're not sure, click 'no'!

If you are sure, click 'yes'!

4. Now get busy having fun!

sharing 101

Make a player disk for a friend so their PC will play any activity disks that you give them.

You will need

- ★ two blank floppy disks
- ★ a friend to send them to

making a player disk

1. Click on the disk icon on the main menu. (This is shown on page 8.)
2. You will be asked if you want to make a player disk or play an activity disk. Click 'make'. Make

making an activity disk

1. Go to the last (finished) screen of the activity you want to save and send. Click on the disk icon on the bottom bar.
2. You will be asked if you want to make a disk to send to a friend. Click 'yes'. Yes

If your friend has 101 easy-peasy things too, you needn't bother with player disks. Follow these steps to...

- ★ play activity disks you make for each other
- ★ test activity disks before sending

1. Click on the disk icon on the main menu. (Shown on page 8.)
2. You will be asked if you want to make a player disk or play an activity disk. Click 'play'. Play
3. Put the player disk into your floppy drive and wait for it to load up.

3 Put a blank disk into your floppy drive and click 'OK'. Ok

4 Wait until the disk is copied, then remove the disk. Click 'OK' to return to the main menu. Ok

5 5. Write 'Player Disk' or 'Activity Disk' on the label.

installing and running an activity disk

Give these instructions to your friend with the disks you've made.

1. Insert the player disk into your floppy drive. Open to find the installer.

2. Launch the installer and follow the on-screen instructions. 'Easy Peasy Player' will now be on your hard disk.

3. Eject the player disk.

4. Launch the player from 'Easy Peasy Player' Program Manager group (PC*) or folder (Mac).

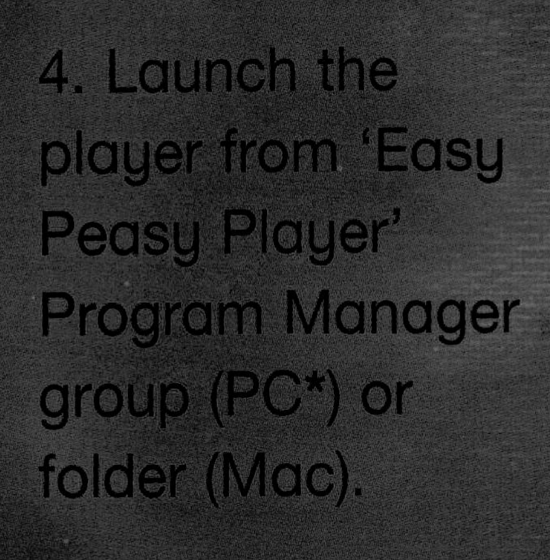

5. Put the activity disk into your floppy drive.

6. Click the disk icon to load the activity.

* Windows '95: 'Start' menu > 'Programs' > 'Easy Peasy Player'.

play on-screen

WOW! All you'll need is your computer and the **101** CD to play all these brilliant activities.

All the activities use the same easy-peasy tools (see below). Play alongside a grown-up until you get the hang of it.

★ postcard

Create a picture postcard using the clip art, write your own message and perhaps even record your own voice.

★ hide and seek

You too can be a computer games designer. Hours of fun!

★ cyberpet corner

Yes, your very own cyberpet – and you decide what it's like.

★ mix and match

A fun memory game to build and play – the better you get, the harder you can make them!

★ music-maker

Become a composer and ace musician. Now you can play the recorder, xylophone and guitar all in the same tune!

★ 101 ideas machine

Spoilt for choice? Let the ideas machine decide what you're going to do next...
(You will need a paint package for some of the on-screen ideas.)

postcards

wish you were here...

Design and send a postcard from your PC to keep in touch with your friends.

You will need

★ a disk to save and send (see page 10)

★ a friend you wish were here

Get started

one click here...	...one here, then	pick a player

1. Choose a background for your card.

Click on the one you like – there are 16 to choose from!

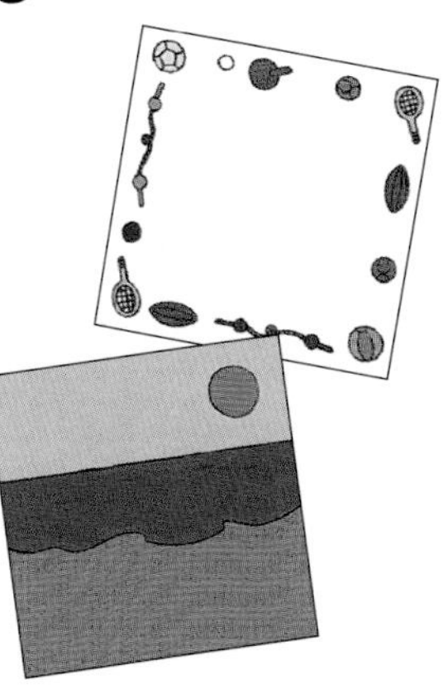

2. Add some pictures.

Make a picture with the clip art. Look out for the ones that move!

3. Write a message.

Drag on numbers, letters or ready-made words.

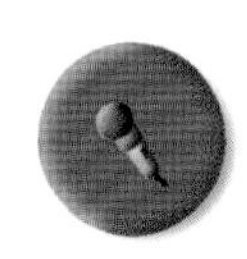

4. Record your own message.

Click on the microphone to record – if you have the right equipment. Ask an adult to help.

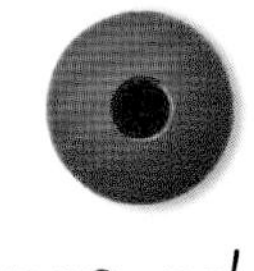

record

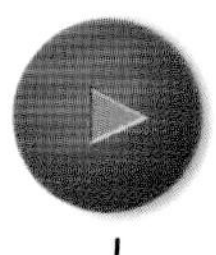

play

stop

Play away!

★ Press the arrow to swap between the picture and message. Make sure you are completely happy with it.

Handy hints

★ To throw away any words and pictures you don't want, drag them into the bin.

★ Use the magic wand to change the size of the pictures.

How many reasons can you think of to send someone a card?

Now it's ready to send!

You can send the card on a disk or print it out and pop it in the post – don't forget the stamp!

make gift tags

You will need

★ printer ★ paper ★ glue stick ★ card ★ scissors ★ coloured pencils ★ hole punch ★ string

1. Open the clip art picker (see page 44) and your paint package (see page 11).
2. Choose some outline clip art.
3. Print out.
4. Glue onto card for strength.
5. Cut out – make the tag shape big enough to write on! Colour in.
6. Punch a hole for the string – watch the edge!

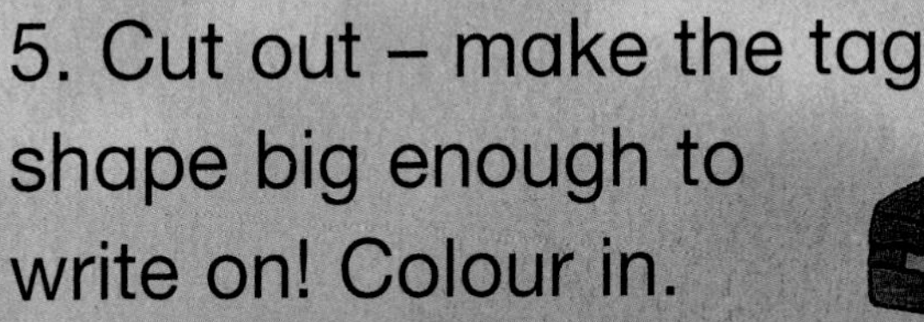

Other software to try ★ Kid Pix Studio ★ Disney Print Studios ★ Jolly PostOffice

hide and seek

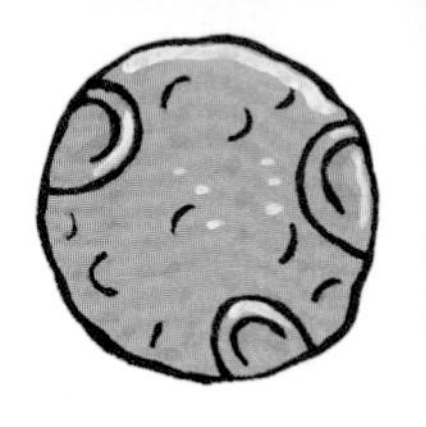

Hide the treasure and set some traps. Then time how long it takes you to reach the treasure.

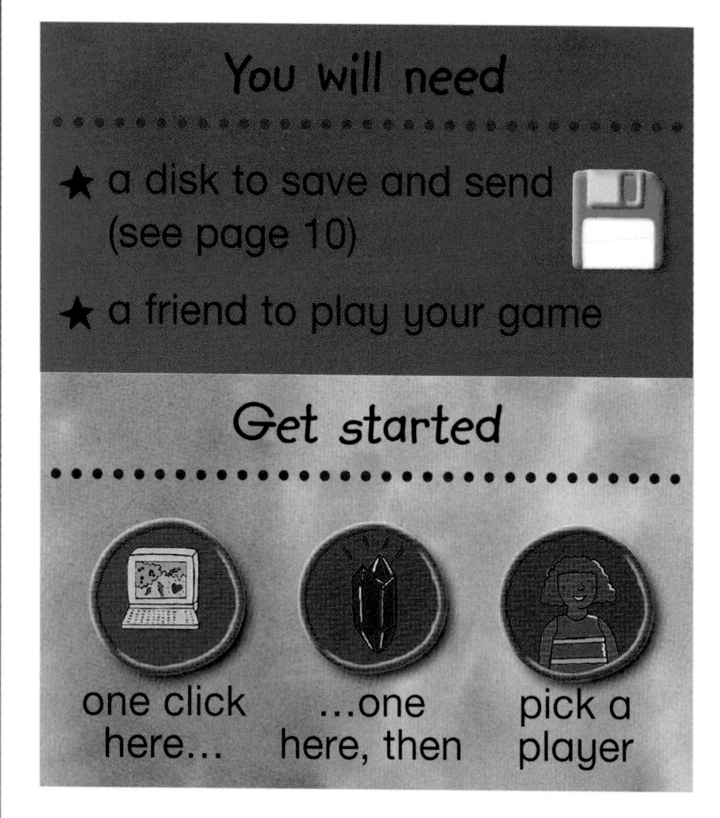

1. Choose a theme.

fairytale

space

wild west

2. Decorate your game.

3. Hide the treasure and the hotspots in the game. These pictures do special things when you land on them!

treasure
first you hide it, then you seek

transporter
this can carry you anywhere!

danger!
this sends you back to the beginning

4. Choose a player.

Now it's ready to play!
You can save the game on a disk for a friend, or play hide and seek straight away!

 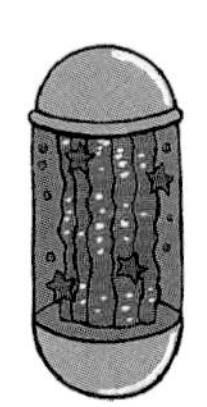     

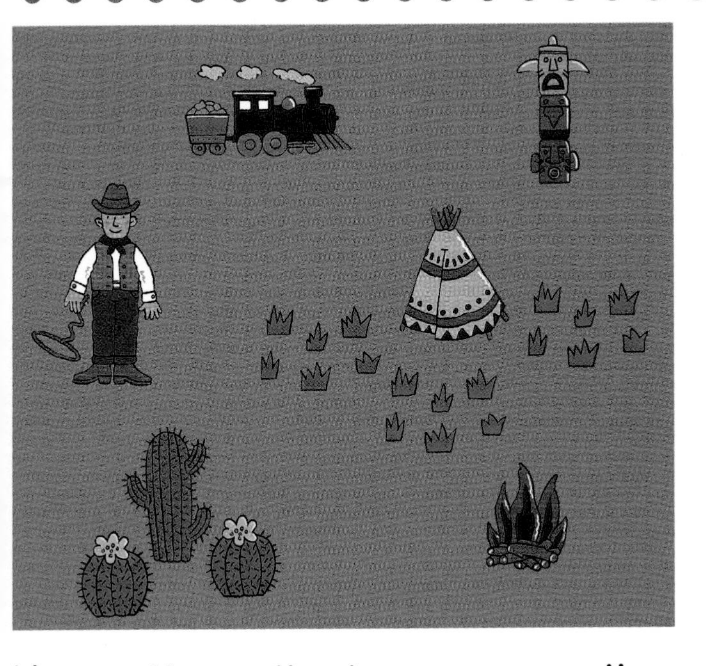

You can't see the treasure – or the hotspots – once you start playing!

Play away

★ Click on an arrow to move one space in that direction. This will start the clock ticking.

★ Try to find the treasure as quickly as possible!

Challenge a friend. Each hides the treasure for the other person. Who's the quickest?

play the cat-and-mouse game

more things to make and do

You will need

★ 9 paper cups ★ paper ★ pencil ★ scissors ★ coloured pencils ★ 5 cm string ★ sticky tape ★ a friend to play the game

1. Copy the mouse shape onto paper, then cut it out.
2. Tape on the string to make a tail.
3. Decorate the cups.

Play away

★ Take turns to hide the mouse under a cup. Don't let your friend see where you hide it!

★ Count how many looks it takes each person to uncover the mouse.

Other software to try ★ Zoombinis ★ Sheila Rae, the Brave ★ PAWS

cyberpet corner

The **101** cyberpet is the cutest computer pet around. You get to choose what it likes best – and what it doesn't like at all. Make one for a friend and see if they can guess how to keep it happy.

1. Where does your new pet like to sleep?

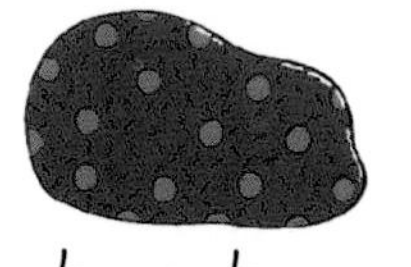

beanbag

nest

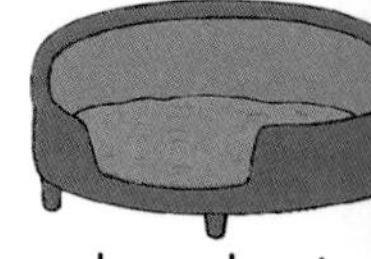

basket

2. What does your new pet like to eat?

pizza

sandwich

apple

3. What does your new pet like to play with?

You will need

- ★ a disk to save and send (see page 10)

- ★ a friend to look after the pet

Get started

one click here...

...one here, then

pick a player

    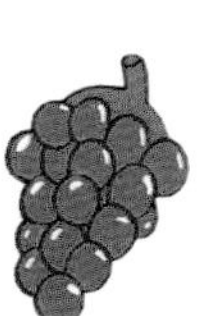   

Now your pet is ready.
You can put your pet away for later, save it on a disk for a friend, or play with it straight away.

★ See what happens if you don't give your pet any food or toys!

Find out what it likes best...

...and what makes it go "Yuck!"

Play away

★ Click on your pet to wake it up or to drag it around the screen.

be a cyberpet designer

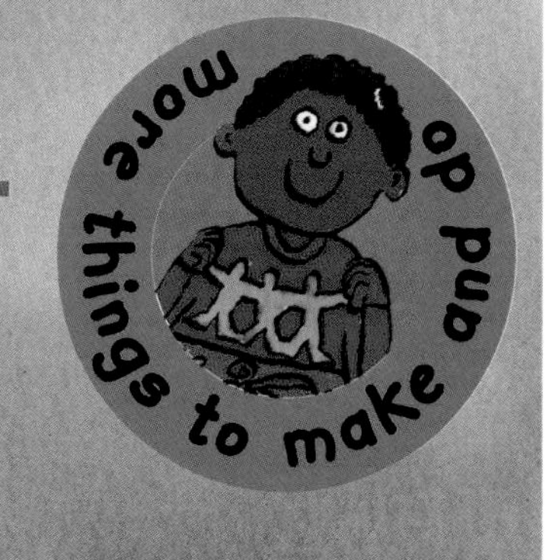

You will need
★ coloured pencils ★ paper

If you could create any creature in the whole world, what would it look like?

Where does your made-up pet come from?

What does it look like when it's little?

Will your pet change as it grows up?

Imagine how it will look when it's old...

mix and match

Are you always forgetting where you've put things? Improve your memory with the mix and match game – or challenge a friend!

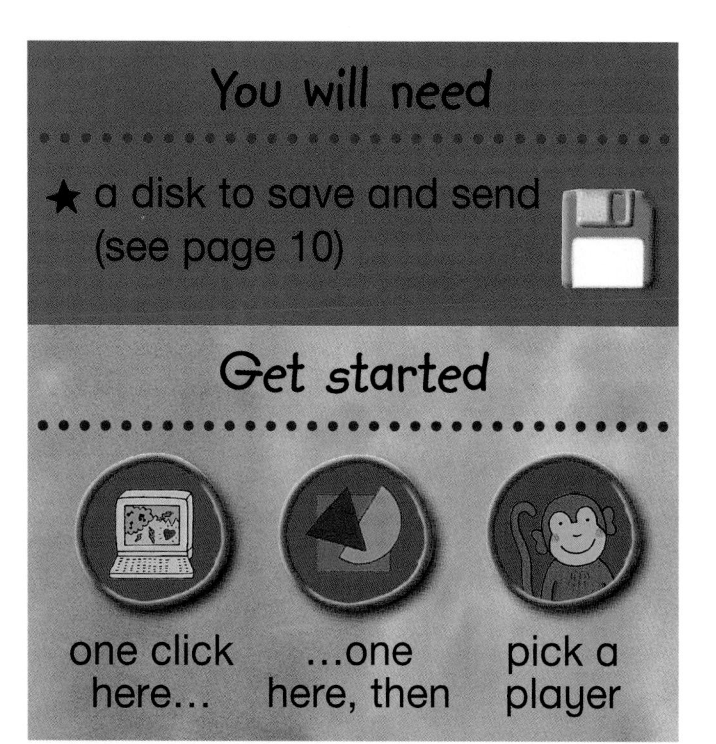

You will need

★ a disk to save and send (see page 10)

Get started

one click here... ...one here, then pick a player

Handy hints

★ Look at where you've put the things on the grid. Do they make a pattern that will help you remember them?

1. Choose what to match.

numbers

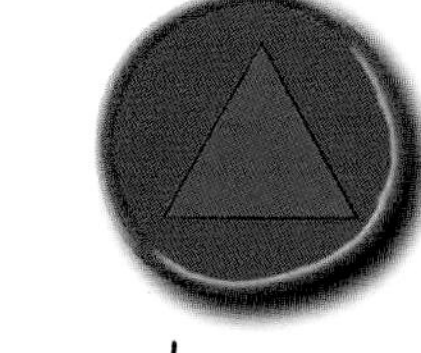

shapes

pictures

2. Choose how hard to make your game.

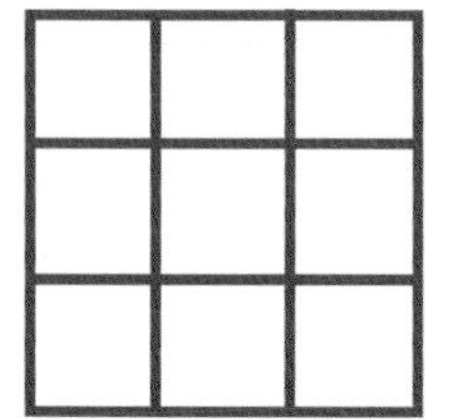

not so hard

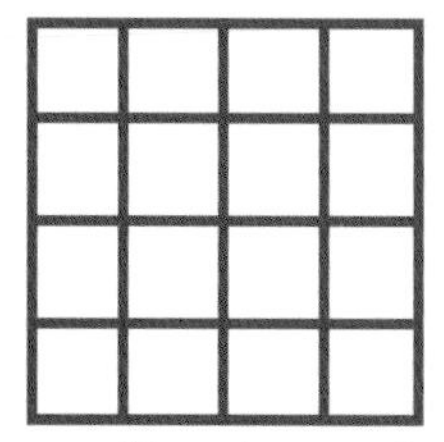

quite hard

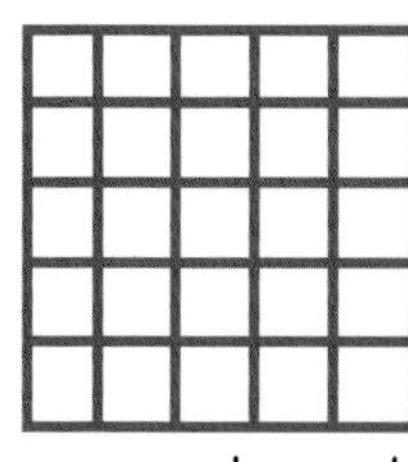

very hard

3. Drag on the items you want to match.

You can use more than one of the same thing if you want.

Now it's ready to play!

You can put your game away for later (to really test your memory), or play it at once. Or send it on a disk for your friend to play.

Play away

★ Press play to hide your mix and match things.

★ Find a match for the thing that appears. If it's a circle, click where you think the circles are. Once you've found all the circles, a new thing will appear for you to find.

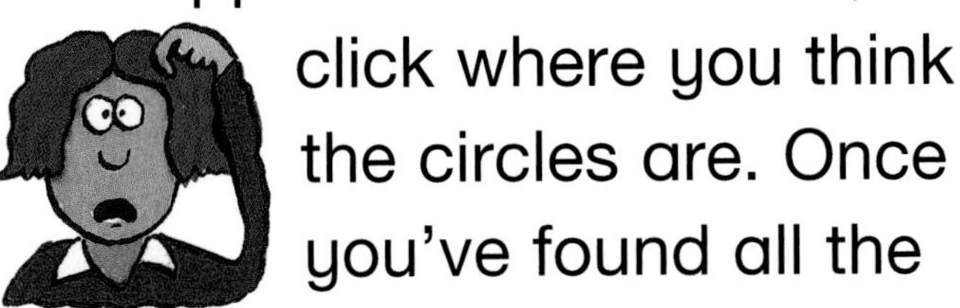

★ The counter shows how many looks you've had, so try to make a 'match' first time!

★ Once you've mastered a game, make yourself a harder one!

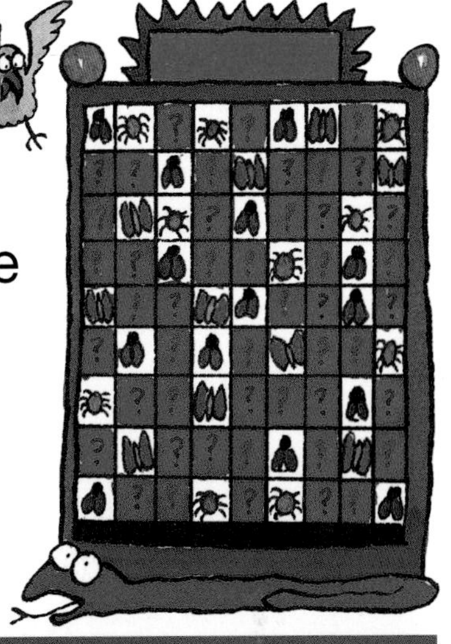

play picture bingo!

You will need

★ card ★ ruler ★ pencil ★ scissors
★ glue stick ★ coloured pencils
★ two friends to play the game

1. Cut out three game-cards (15 x 10 cm).
2. Glue six pictures (5 x 5 cm) to each card. Make each picture different.
3. Make a 'match' for each picture.

Play away

★ Each player has a game-card.

★ Put the matching pictures face down. Take turns to pick one. If it matches one on your card, place it on top. If not, put it under the pile.

★ The first to cover all the images on their card wins, and shouts 'Bingo!'

Other software to try ★ Thinkin' Things ★ Playskool Puzzles ★ Millie's Math House

music-maker

Even if you can't play an instrument, you can use your computer to make music. Write your own tune or copy one of these.

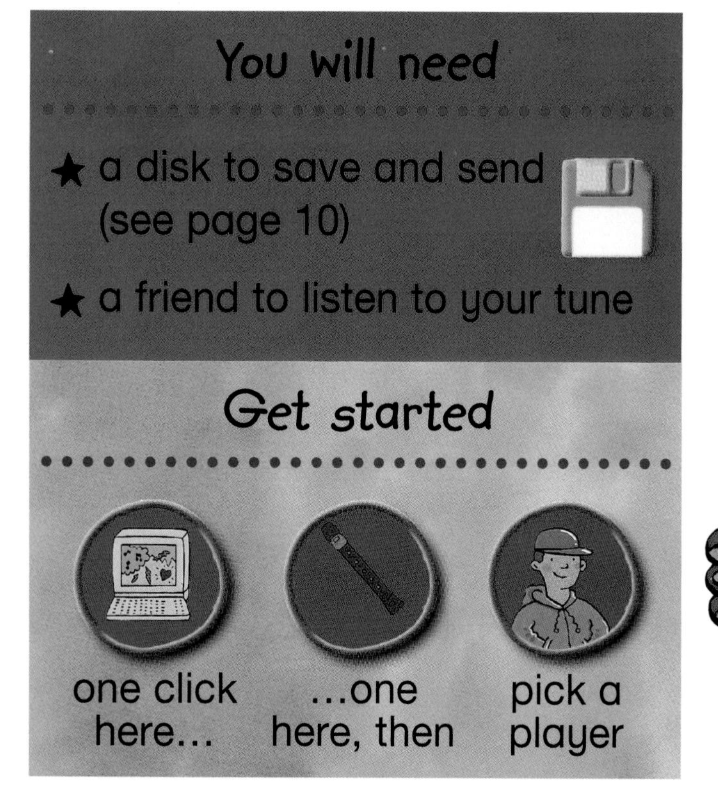

You will need

★ a disk to save and send (see page 10)

★ a friend to listen to your tune

Get started

one click here... ...one here, then pick a player

1. Choose an instrument.

2. Add some notes.

Run your mouse over the notes to hear them and click to add them. You can switch between instruments in the same song if you like.

Handy hints

★ You can drag your notes up and down to alter your tune.

Now it's finished!

You can put your tune away for later, save it on a disk for a friend, or play it back at once.

Play away

plays your tune

stops your tune

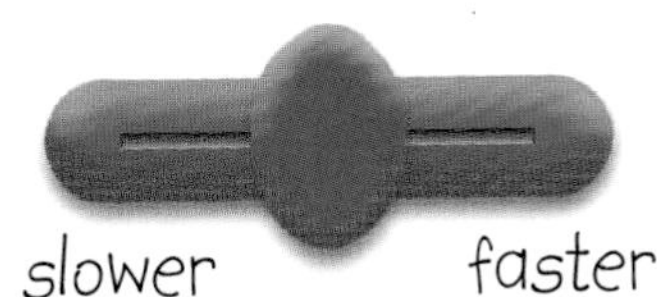

alters the speed

more songs to play

more things to make and do

Copy the notes below carefully to play these favourite tunes on your computer.

Twinkle, twinkle

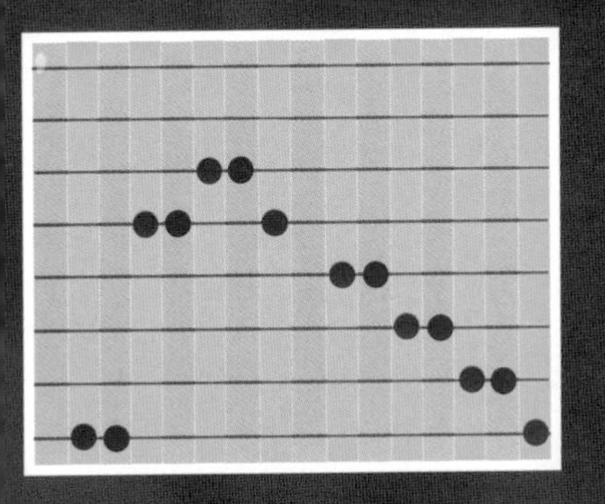

Frère Jacques

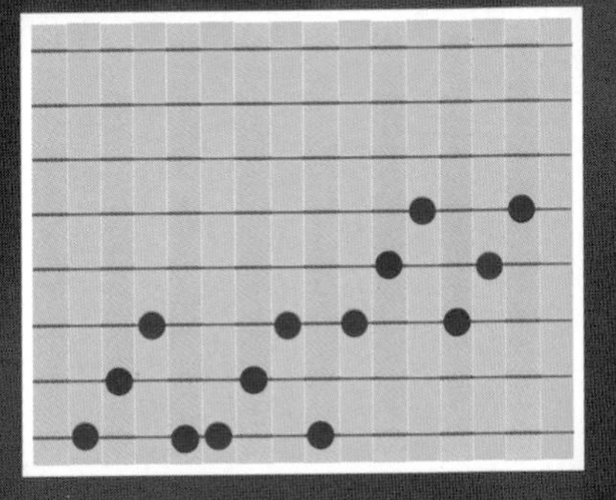

Three blind mice

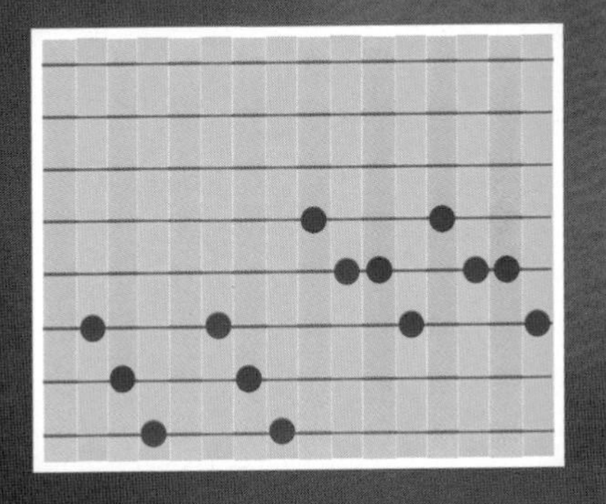

Au clair de la lune

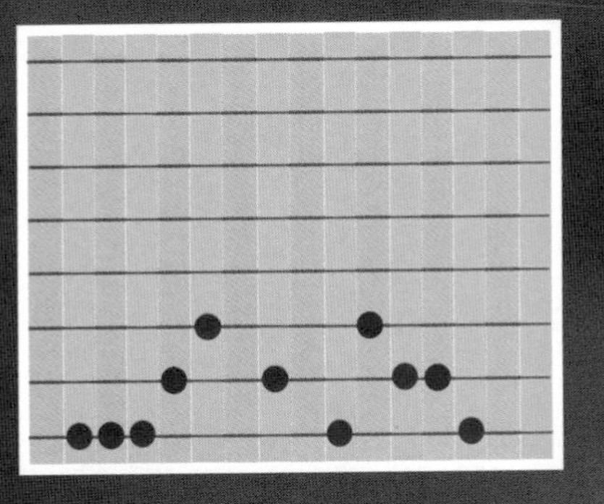

Good King Wenceslas

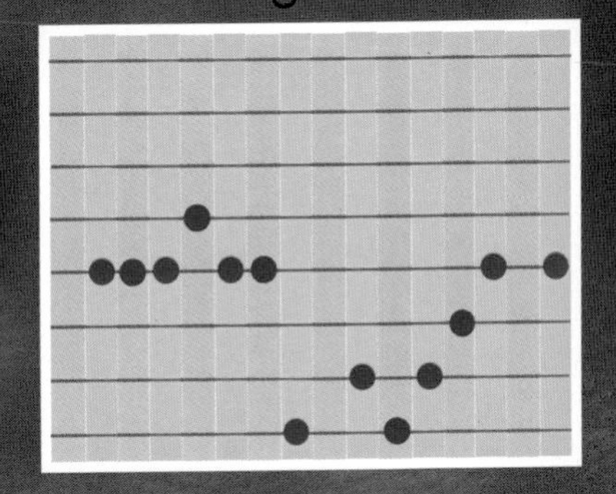

Happy birthday

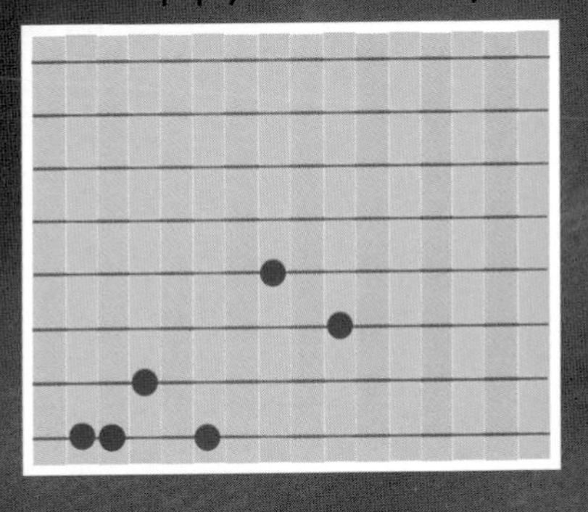

101 ideas machine

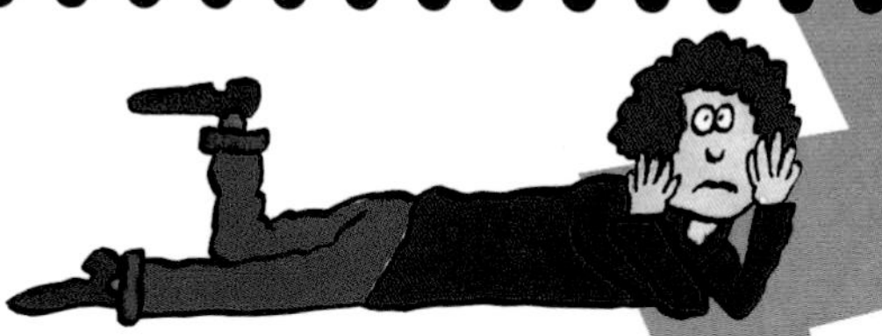

Are you bored? Maybe you just can't decide what to do? The **101** ideas machine is sure to come up with some neat ideas.

Play away

1. Click on the handle to start the ideas machine.
It will crunch out an idea. If you don't feel like doing the idea on the card, click the handle to get another one.

2. There are 101 ideas* for:

★ *easy-peasy projects*
press the play button to start

Play

★ *fun things to do with – or without – your computer*
just follow the instructions

★ *hilarious jokes to tell*
click on the card to see the punchline

*** Every idea is numbered**

101 things to do!

There really are **101** easy-peasy things just waiting for you – so get busy!

Use the clip art picker to:

Make a 'Keep Out!' sign for your bedroom.

Make some wallpaper for your dolls house.

Make a set of matching cards and play 'Snap!'

In your paint package:

Draw your favourite animal going on holiday.

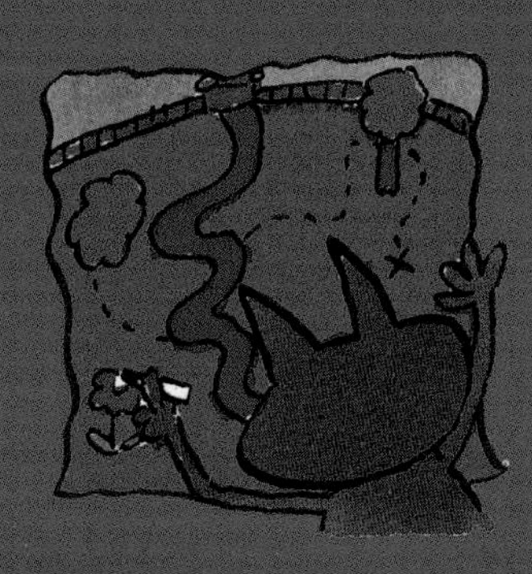

Make a map of your garden.

Draw your cyberpet going to the moon.

Use **101** easy-peasy things to:

Make a spooky tune with the music-maker.

Dress a rabbit pirate. Why not make him a treasure island?

Make a number spinner and play 'Spin and win!'

Other software to try ★ Pingu ★ Jolly Postmans Party ★ 101 Amazing Things

print-and-play

With just these six activities, you can design and print at least **101** different things to play with. Some of them make great presents, too!

colouring in

Whatever you decide to print, ask a grown-up to set your printer in Parents' Corner. Even if you have a colour printer, you might want to print out black outlines, so that you can have fun colouring in.

You might need

- ★ coloured pencils
- ★ coloured crayons
- ★ coloured felt-tips
- ★ coloured paints (and brushes)
- ★ collage scraps and PVA glue
- ★ fabric scraps and fabric glue

★ finger puppets

There are 40 different finger puppets to print and make – and even more variety when you start colouring them in! Can YOU think up a puppet theatre play that stars a lion, a mermaid and a juggler?!

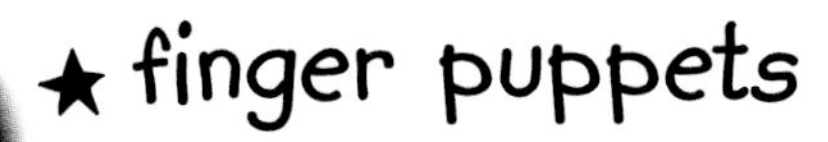

★ dressing up

Choose one of the figures and dress them up with the amazing print-out outfits. (You could glue scraps of old material onto the clothes instead of colouring them in.) Be silly or stylish – it's up to you!

★ mobiles

Don't count sheep at night – count how many of these easy-peasy mobiles you can fit on your ceiling!

★ masks

Mix and match the mask features to create all sorts of weird and wonderful masks to wear.

★ spinners

These colour and number spinners are easy to make. There are wizard whizzers too!

★ party pack

Design your own matching party stationery – invitations, badges for your guests, place names and party bags.

finger puppets

Would you like to put on your own show? Start by having some 'actors' at your fingertips!

You will need

★ printer ★ paper ★ card
★ scissors ★ glue stick

Get started

one click here… …one here, then pick a player

1. Choose a theme.

fantasy

circus

animals

2. Pick some puppets.

You can have up to four at once.

Make up a story about your puppets. You could put on a show for your friends.

Make away!

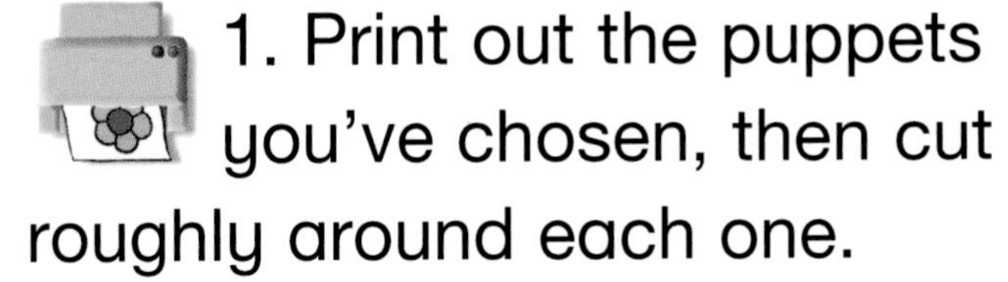

1. Print out the puppets you've chosen, then cut roughly around each one.

2. Glue them onto card. You can miss out this step, but your puppets won't be very strong.

3. Cut out carefully – don't cut off the tabs!

4. Fold along the dotted line.

5. Curl the tab around your finger and stick down with glue. (You may need some help from a friend.)

6. Fold back the other tab and stick.

Can you fit a puppet on each finger?

make a mitten monster

You will need

★ an old woolly glove ★ fabric glue ★ fabric scraps ★ lengths of wool ★ blunt darning needle

1. Cut some monstrous features out of fabric.
2. Glue the features on the glove and leave to dry.
3. Ask an adult to help you thread through the strands of woolly 'hair' as shown. Knot in place.
4. Scare someone silly!

finger puppets

Other software to try ★ Crayola Magic Wardrobe ★ Kid Pix Studio ★ Disney Print Studios

dressing up

Choose a figure to dress up. You could make a ballerina, a pirate, a witch…or something *very* silly indeed!

You will need

★ printer ★ paper ★ card
★ glue stick ★ scissors

Get started

one click here… …one here, then pick a player

1. Choose a figure.

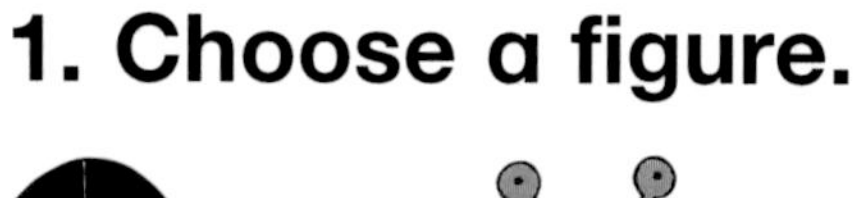

Handy hints

★ Use the magic wand to change the figure's skin (or fur!) colour.
Use it to change the pattern or colour of the clothes, too.

2. Add some clothes.

tops

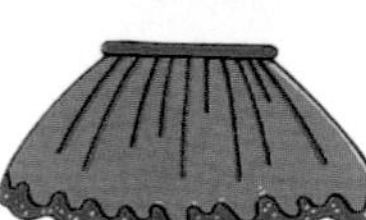
bottoms

shoes

hats

special extras

Make away!

1. Print out your file.

2. Cut out the figure, clothes and stand along the dotted lines. Don't cut off the tabs! Glue the figure and the stand onto card to make them strong.

3. Glue the two pieces of the stand together like this.

4. Fold over all the tabs on the clothes, then dress up your figure.

Why not make clothes in different sizes? Ask an adult to help you change the print size.

patterns and prints

From catwalk to football pitch, lots of clothes have patterns – and someone has the job of designing them.

more things to make and do

Collect some leaves and brush them with paint. Press them paint-side down on a sheet of paper. Does the leaf make the same pattern with both sides? Now experiment with other 'printing blocks'...

Other software to try ★ Barbie Fashion Designer ★ Crayola Magic Wardrobe ★ Kid Pix Studio

mobiles

Mobiles are fun to look at and not difficult to make. You may need some help from a grown-up to make and string your mobile.

You will need

★ printer ★ paper ★ glue stick ★ cotton thread ★ scissors ★ sticky tape ★ ruler

Get started

one click here...

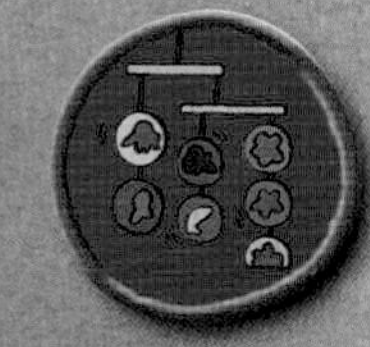

...one here, then

pick a player

1. Choose the pictures for your mobile. Drag them on.

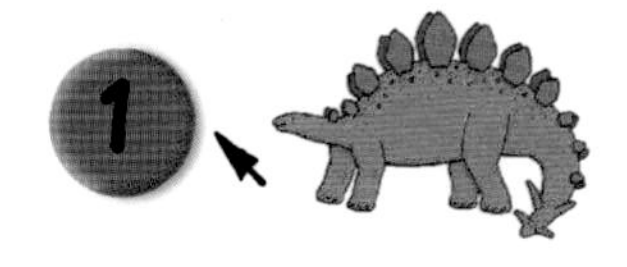

1 dinosaurs

2 animals

3 birthday

4 Christmas

2. Choose a pattern for the hanging beams.

Make away!

1. Print out your file and cut out all the shapes.

2. Fold four of the circles. Snip a hole in the middle of the fold as shown.

3. Cut three 40-cm threads. Tape one to each of the other three circles.

4. Fold and glue each circle back-to-back.

5. String the other circles through the holes you cut. Glue back-to-back.

6. Fold along the dotted lines on each beam. Glue to make a stiff support.

7. Tie the mobile pieces to the beams as shown.

8. Tie the four-picture beam to the other beam from its middle.

Handy hints

★ Slide the cotton along the centre of the lower beam until your mobile balances.

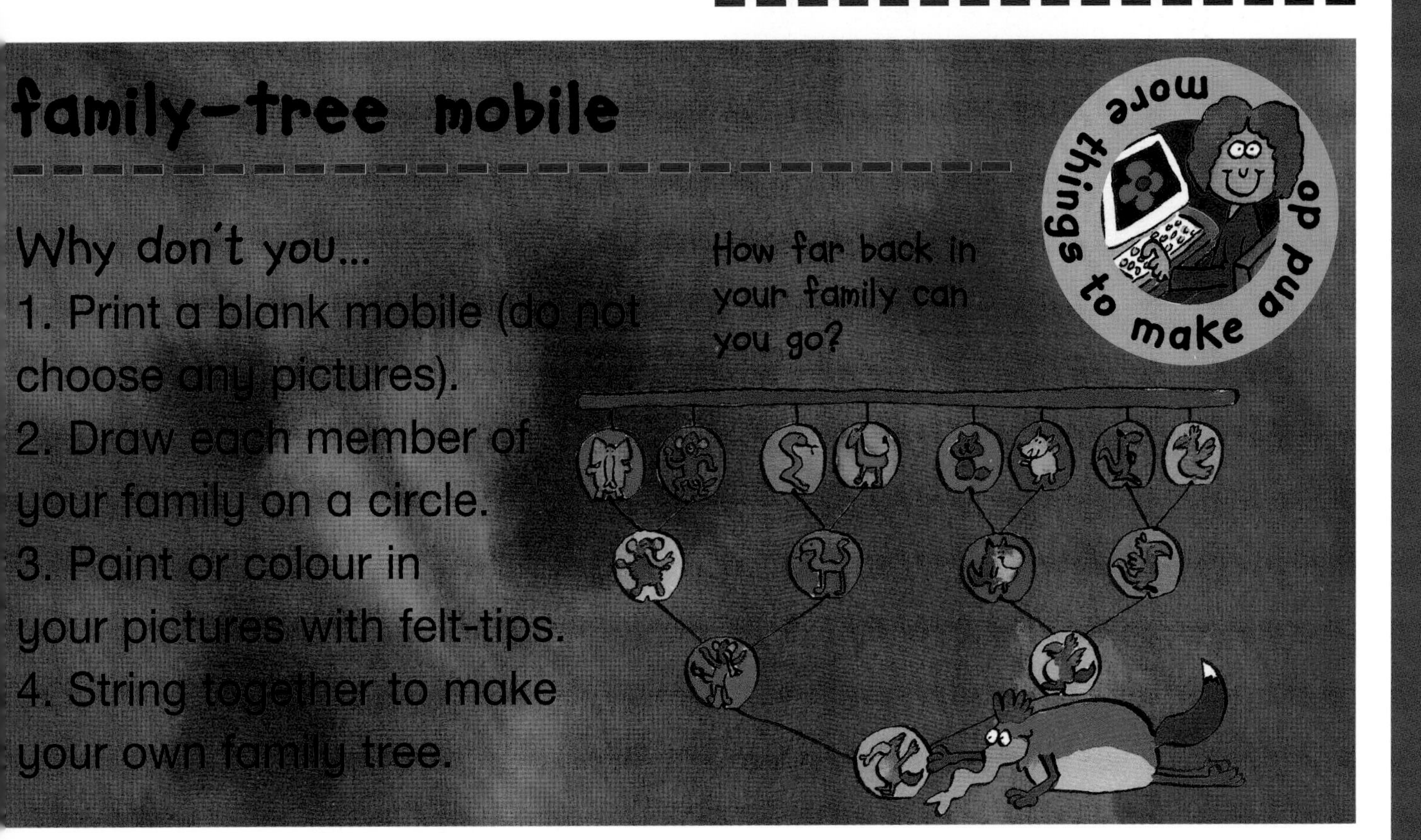

family-tree mobile

more things to make and do

Why don't you...

1. Print a blank mobile (do not choose any pictures).
2. Draw each member of your family on a circle.
3. Paint or colour in your pictures with felt-tips.
4. String together to make your own family tree.

How far back in your family can you go?

masks

Disguise yourself as a scary monster! Use your computer to design some amazing masks.

You will need

★ printer ★ paper ★ thin card
★ glue stick ★ scissors
★ elastic ★ sticky tape

Get started

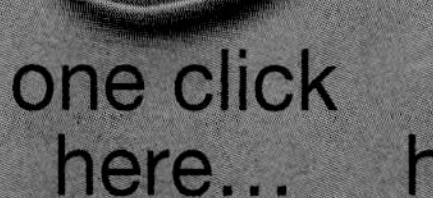

one click here... ...one here, then pick a player

1. Click on a mask shape.
There are six to choose from.

2. Click to choose spots or stripes.
(Or keep your mask plain.)

3. Choose a nose, a snout or a beak.
There are six different ones.

4. Choose some ears.
There are six of these, too!

5. Click to add the finishing touches.
Eyebrows, feelers or whiskers?

Handy hints

★ Use the magic wand to change the colour of your mask and its features.

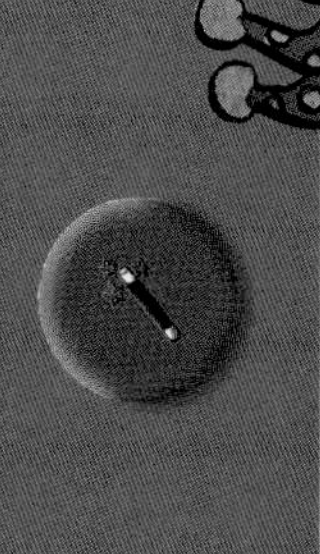

Make away

1. Print out your file.
2. Glue onto card for strength.

3. Carefully cut out the mask and nose.
4. Tape on the nose. Make sure it can flap about so you can breathe.

5. Punch a hole on each side, for the elastic to go through.

make up an animal story

more things to make and do

You can invent really strange animals for your masks. Make up a story about them.

Are they friendly to each other?

Where do they live?
somewhere warm?
somewhere cold?

What do they eat?*
beetles?
frogs?
tomatoes?
magnets?
children?

How do they move?
prowl? slither?
belly-dance? hop?
hover? swim?

What noises do they make?
snort? squeak?
buzz? groan?

*NEVER eat beetles, frogs (unless they're cooked), magnets OR other children. (It's OK to eat tomatoes, though.)

Other software to try ★ Awesome Animated Monster Maker ★ Kid Pix Studio ★ Disney Print Studios

spinners

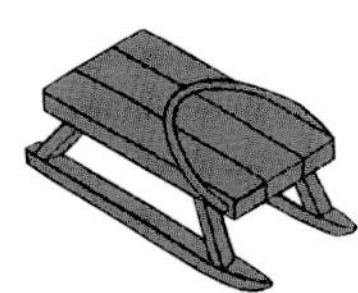

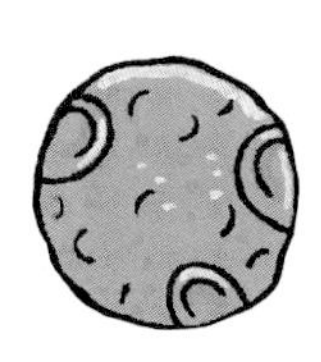

Whizz some whizzers to see what happens when colours swirl and mix. Or make number spinners to use in your games, instead of dice.

You will need

★ printer ★ paper ★ glue stick ★ scissors ★ pencil stub or stick (spinners) ★ string and blunt darning needle (whizzers)

Get started

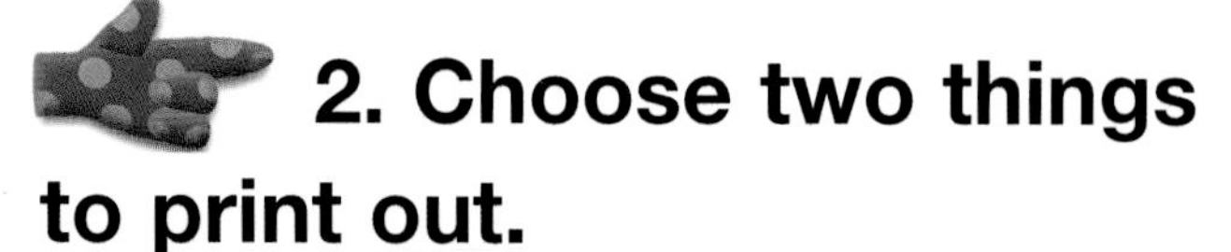

one click here... ...one here, then pick a player

1. Choose spinning tops or whizzers.

spinners whizzers

2. Choose two things to print out.

There are eight different patterns to choose from.

Handy hints

★ Use the magic wand to change the colours.

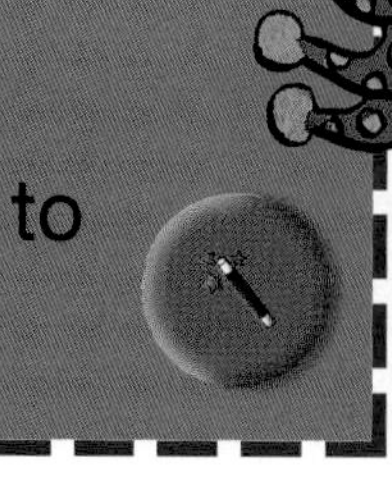

Make away!

1. Print out your file.

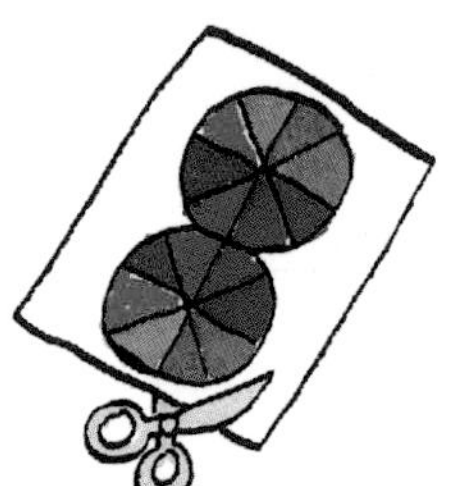

2. Cut out around the solid lines.

3. Fold along the dotted line and glue back-to-back.

Spinners

★ Push the pencil or stick through the hole at the centre of the disk.

★ Keep the disk low on the pencil.

★ Spin your spinner on a smooth, flat surface.

Whizzers

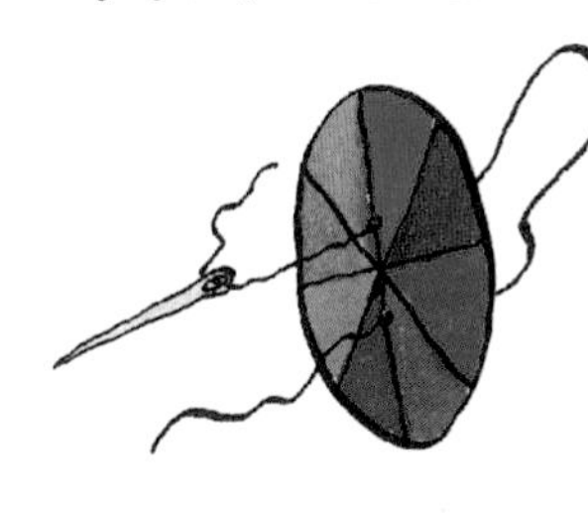

★ Thread the string through the holes as shown and tie.

★ Keep the disk in the middle of the loop as you twist, then whizz!

If it will not spin properly, add another disk for extra weight.

be a colour magician

Use blank spinners to learn all about mixing colours.

You will need

★ blank spinners

★ red, yellow, blue, white and black poster paints

★ paintbrush

What happens if you paint your spinner...

red + yellow?

red + blue?

blue + yellow?

red + black?

black + white?

Spin to find out!

party pack

It's party time! Use your computer to make your party extra-special.

1. Choose a picture for your party pack.

 animals

 festivals

 fantasy

 party

 **2. Choose a shape to frame your picture.**
There are four to choose from.

 **3. Click on a background colour.**
There are six to choose from.

 **4. Write a name for your party.**
Drag the letters onto the lines. You could spell out your own name, or write down what sort of theme your party will have.

5. Click on the things you want to print.

Choose an invitation, a party bag, a badge, a place name – or all four!

invitations

Fold along the dotted lines, fill in the details and send.

Make away!

1. Print your party pack.

2. Cut around the solid lines.

party bag

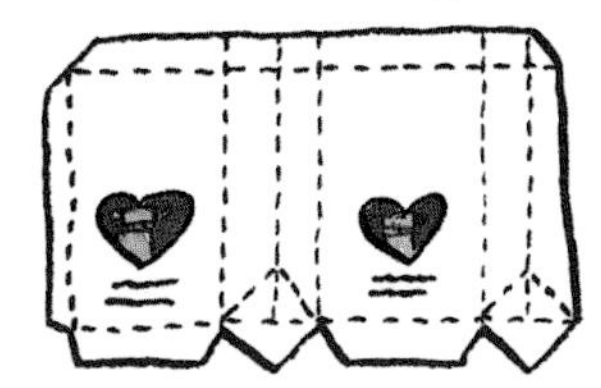

Fold along all the dotted lines as shown.

Glue or tape the two sides together.

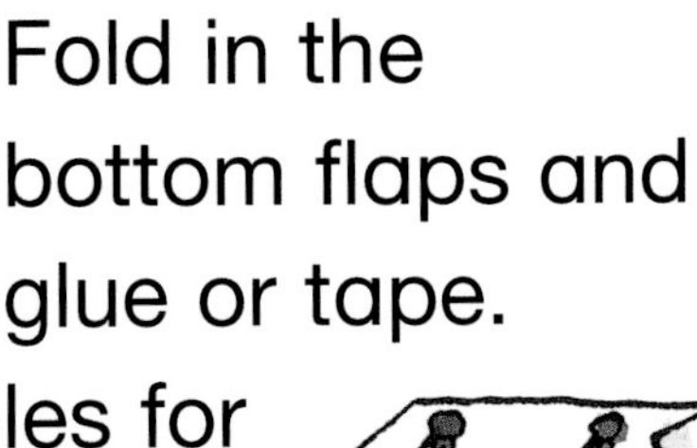

Fold in the bottom flaps and glue or tape.

Punch out holes for the handles, and knot lengths of wool in place as shown.

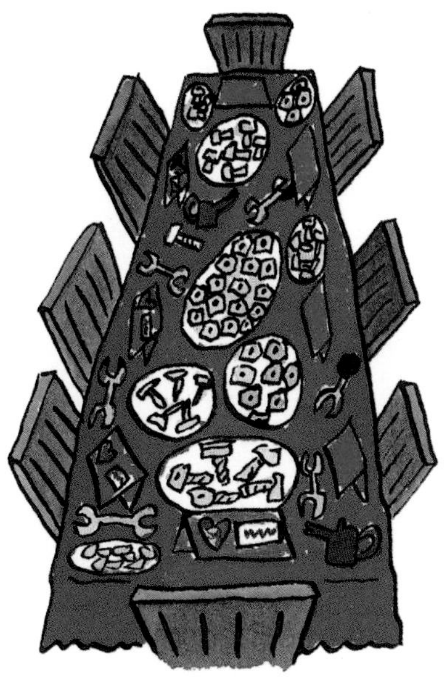

place names

Fold along the dotted lines. Stand your place names on the table for your party feast!

badges

To make the badge extra-strong, glue onto card first. Tape a safety pin to the back of the badge. (Be careful when pinning!)

play on-line

101 fast links take you to interesting sites to visit out on the Internet.

You will need

- ★ a modem
- ★ a Web browser
- ★ a service connection (such as AOL, Compuserve or Demon)

1. Launch your browser and connect to the Internet.

2. From inside your browser, use the 'File' menu to open the 'Easy Peasy' folder on your hard drive, and then open the file called 'online.htm'.

3. Now choose from the menu to explore the three groups.

The fast links were all correct at time of going to press. The on-line locations may have changed since. If you have problems, try linking up through a search engine, such as Yahoo.

kids' sites
Explore these fast links to find games, jokes, activities and loads of fun!

more links
Use the links to discover more brilliant sites for children.

parents' sites
These sites were specially selected for parents using the Internet.

be an on-line explorer

There are far more than **101** exciting places to visit on-line. Why don't you go and try to...

...find out everything you can about your favourite animal

...find your favourite sports star or team

...find your favourite theme park

...find a place of worship

...find some games and puzzles to play

...go and visit a museum in another country

clip art

With the **101** clip art picker, you can use any of these pictures in your own work – as often as you like.

Get started

click* here (and launch your paint package)

1. Choose the type of clip art you want to use.
There are six groups, shown on the six panels on these pages.

2. Choose a picture.

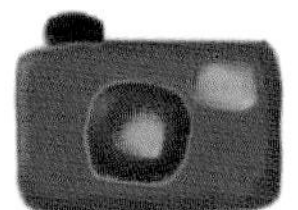

Click on the camera to take a snap. Change to outline first if you want to colour in.

3. Paste in your picture.
Click on your page first so you are in your paint package, not the clip art picker. Go to the 'Edit' menu and choose 'paste'.

Handy hints

- ★ Use your paint package tools to scale and resize your picture – and to colour it in.
- ★ Paste again and again to create repeating patterns.
- ★ Why not rotate (spin) or reflect (mirror) the clip art?

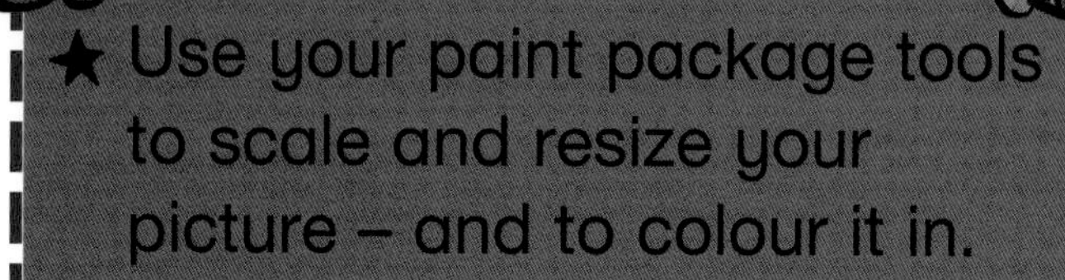

* Two clicks for Windows 3.1 or Macintosh users; one click if you open from the Windows 95 'Start' menu.

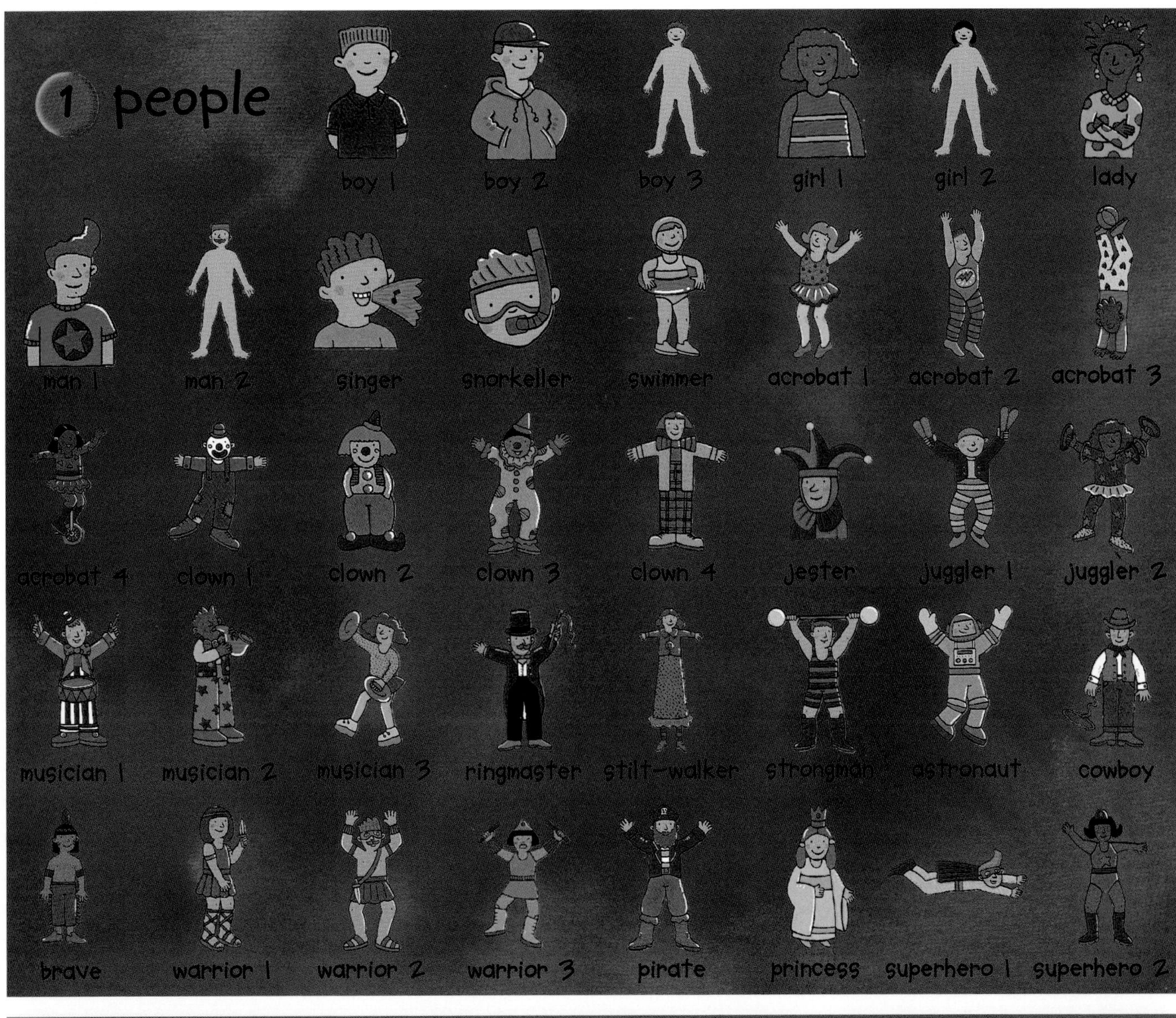

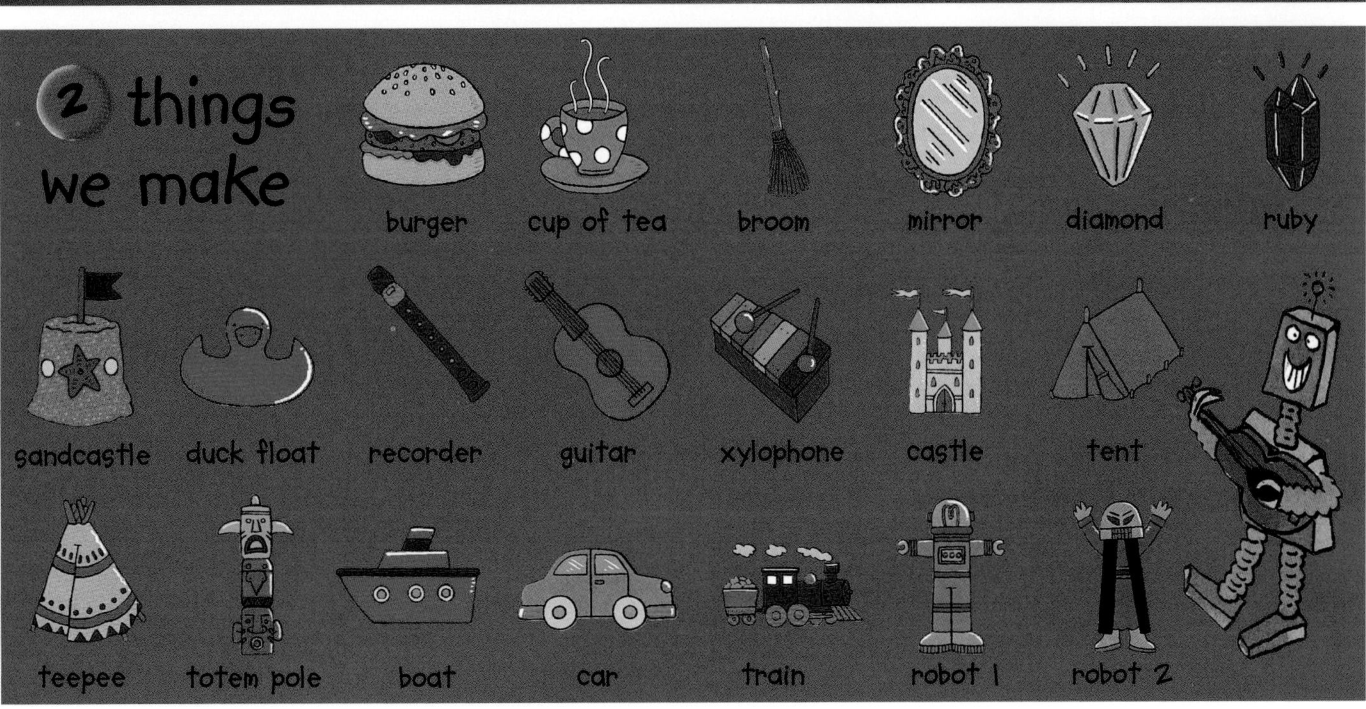

Other software to try ★ Kid Pix Studio ★ ClarisWorks for Kids ★ ClickArt

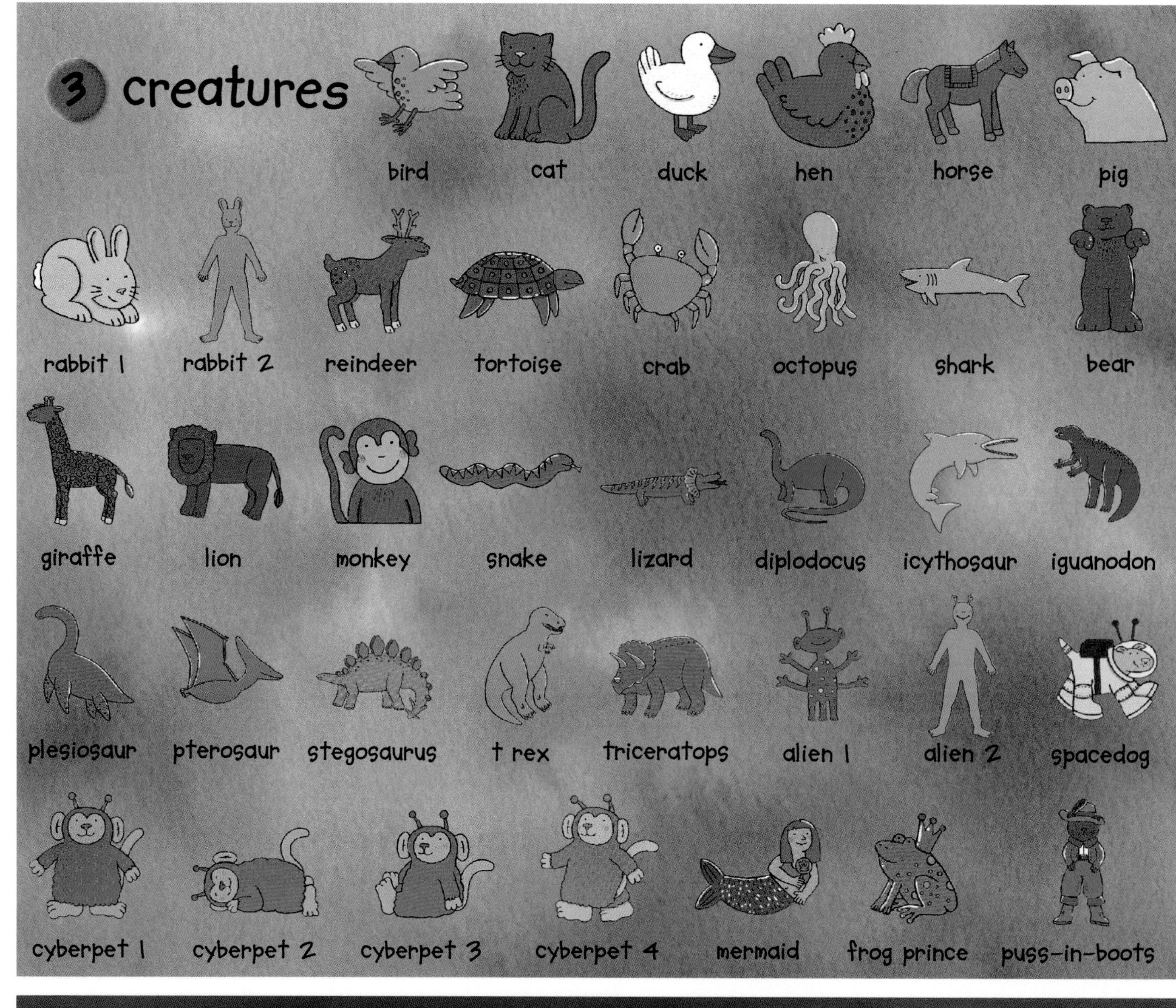
3 creatures
bird
cat
duck
hen
horse
pig
rabbit 1
rabbit 2
reindeer
tortoise
crab
octopus
shark
bear
giraffe
lion
monkey
snake
lizard
diplodocus
icythosaur
iguanodon
plesiosaur
pterosaur
stegosaurus
t rex
triceratops
alien 1
alien 2
spacedog
cyberpet 1
cyberpet 2
cyberpet 3
cyberpet 4
mermaid
frog prince
puss-in-boots

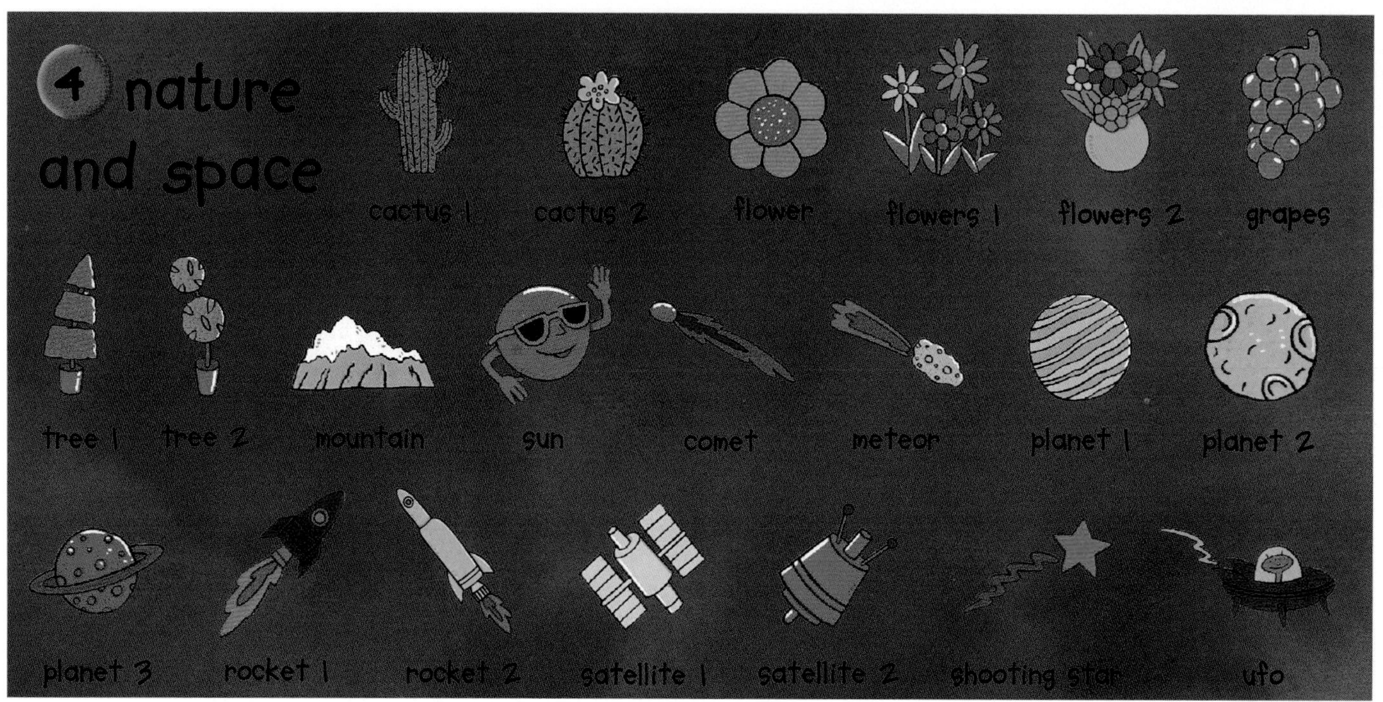
4 nature and space
cactus 1
cactus 2
flower
flowers 1
flowers 2
grapes
tree 1
tree 2
mountain
sun
comet
meteor
planet 1
planet 2
planet 3
rocket 1
rocket 2
satellite 1
satellite 2
shooting star
ufo

5 festival!

6 clothes

glossary

application or program Software which contains all the instructions your computer needs to do things, such as painting, counting or writing.

CD-ROM Compact disk used to store computer data as well as music. You need a special CD drive and software to allow your computer to read CD-ROMs.

click, double-click Clicking is used to select and control items on screen. Press your mouse button to click. Clicking twice opens the file you have pointed to.

close A command for shutting a window. Do this by choosing the close command from the file menu or by clicking in the top left-hand corner of the window.

cursor The screen pointer that you move around with the mouse and use to select, move and control icons on your desktop.

cut, copy and paste Having selected something from a document, you can cut it or copy it and then paste it down again in the same document or a new one.

drag If you keep the mouse pressed down when you click on an object on the screen, you can move or drag it around your desktop.

e-mail (electronic mail) When two computers are connected to the internet, distance is no object. Your computer can send messages electronically down the phone line to a mailbox inside another computer.

file A set of instructions that tells your computer what to do. There are two types of file: applications or documents.

floppy disk Used to store your work and move it from one computer to another. The 'floppy' part is inside a hard plastic case to keep it safe.

font A set of characters with a particular look or style to use in your word-processor or paint package.

icon A little picture that is used to represent a file or folder on your computer desktop. Double-click to open or launch it.

internet A worldwide network of computers connected together by telephone. You need a modem and special software to connect up to it.

memory Your computer has two sorts of memory, measured in bytes. RAM memory is for quick reference, and hard disk memory is for storing files away.

menu A quick way of showing all the choices or tools available in a program. Menus appear when you click on words on the menu bar.

mouse or trackball Pointers with buttons that are used to move the cursor around and allow you to control your computer.

on-line You are on-line when your computer is connected up to the internet via a modem.

open Double-clicking opens a file so that you can view it or work on it. You could also choose 'open' from the file menu.

pc (personal computer) A PC is any personal computer. But PC is also used to refer to only IBM compatibles that run Microsoft Windows system software.

printer A machine that takes data from your computer to write text or draw pictures onto paper for you. Some can print in colour.

save To store or record some information for future use. Always make more than one copy so you have back-up in case one copy gets damaged.

screen saver Software that protects your screen when you are not working at your computer. It saves you having to keep turning your PC off and on.

software The instructions that tell a computer what to do (rather than the hardware that makes up the computer system).

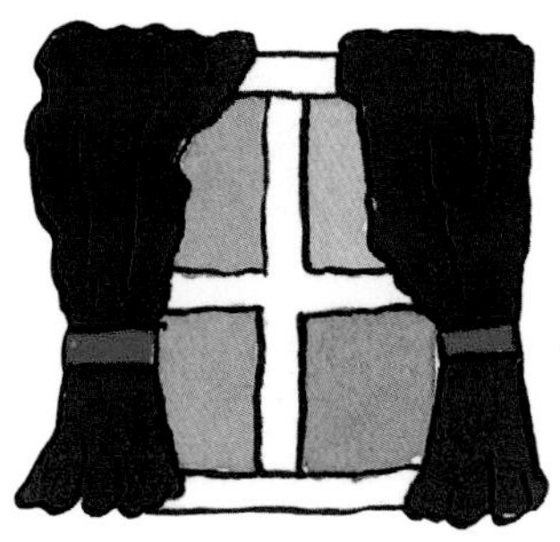

window The frame that surrounds an open document. It is called a window because it lets you look in on your work.

world wide web Network, or web, of information published on pages and accessed through the internet.

useful addresses

organisations

British Educational Communications and Technology agency (BECTa)
Milburn Hill Road, Science Park, Coventry CV4 7JJ
☎ 01203 416 994
http://www.becta.org.uk

Scottish Council for Educational Technology (SCET)
74 Victoria Crescent Road, Glasgow G12 9NJ
☎ 0141 337 5000
http://www.scet.org.uk

Parent's Information Network (PIN)
☎ 0181 248 4666

hardware manufacturers

Apple Computer UK Ltd
Information Service
☎ 0800 127 753
http://www.apple.com

Compaq Computer Ltd
☎ 0181 332 3000
http://www.compaq.com

IBM (UK) Ltd
☎ 01703 265 181
http://www.pc.ibm.com

software suppliers

TAG Developments Ltd
☎ 01474 357 350
email sales@tagdev.co.uk

software publishers

Brøderbund Europe
☎ 01429 520 250
http://www.broderbund.com

Claris UK
☎ 0345 413 060
http://www.claris.com

Microsoft Ltd
☎ 01734 270 002
http://www.microsoft.com/uk

publications

PC Guide
Future Publishing
☎ 01225 442 244
http://www.futurenet.com

PC Home
IDG Media Ltd
☎ 01625 878 888
http://www.idg.co.uk/parents